Usborne

First Sticker Book

Museums

Illustrated by Wesley Robins

Woolly mammoth

You'll find all the stickers
at the back of the book.

Giraffe

Butterflies

Rhinoceros model

Words by Holly Bathie

Designed by Matt Durber and Yasmin Faulkner

Museums

A museum is an amazing collection of things from the past. Many museums, like this one, have mummies, statues and other things from Ancient Egypt in them. Can you add all the stickers to finish this picture?

PYRAMID MODEL

SPHINX MODEL

OBELISK

CANOPIC JARS

THE
GODDESS
BASTET

SARCOPHAGUS

THE
GOD
ANUBIS

ANUBIS

Science museum

A science museum tells you all about things that people have discovered or invented, from faraway planets to fantastic robots.

ENGINEERING

NEPTUNE

How do gears work?

FORCES

VAN DE GRAAFF GENERATOR

TELESCOPE

URANUS

SATURN

JUPITER

MARS

EARTH

VENUS

MERCURY

SUN

SATELLITE

SHUTTLE

DNA MODEL

SPACESUIT

SPACE ROCKET

ATOM MODEL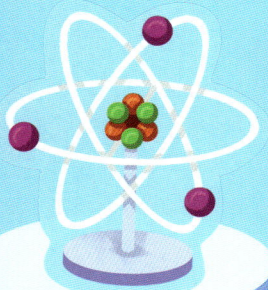

SPACE

LUNAR ROVER

Natural history museum

Here you can find out about plants, animals and the incredible story of life on Earth. This is the dinosaur room full of skeletons, fossils and dinosaur footprints.

Ankylosaurus

Dimorphodon

Plesiosaur

TIMELINE

Tyrannosaurus rex skeleton

Fossils

Pterodactyl

Prehistoric globe

Dinosaur footprints

Aegyptosaurus
skeleton

Stegosaurus
model

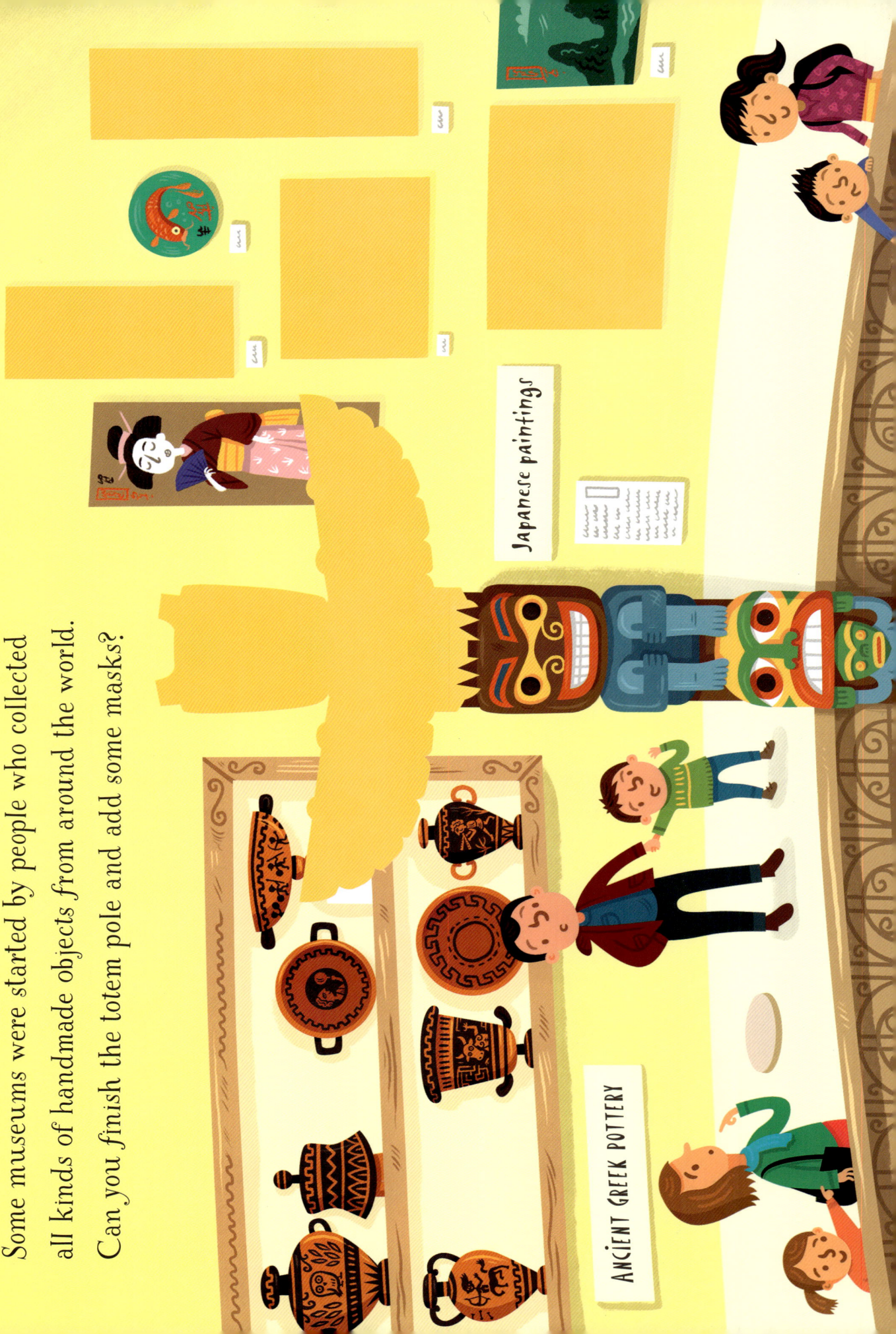

Around the world

Some museums were started by people who collected
all kinds of handmade objects from around the world.

Can you finish the totem pole and add some masks?

Japanese paintings

ANCIENT GREEK POTTERY

African musical instruments

Native American totem pole

Masks through the ages

Transport museum

This museum tells the story of transport with cars, buses, trains, planes and other old vehicles. Add some more to the scene.

Light helicopter

Omnibus

1921 Dennis fire engine

Marshall steam engine

Motorcycle and sidecar

Formula 1 car

Lancaster bomber

Bristol Boxkite

Tiltrotor plane

Steam engine

Ford Model T
motorcar

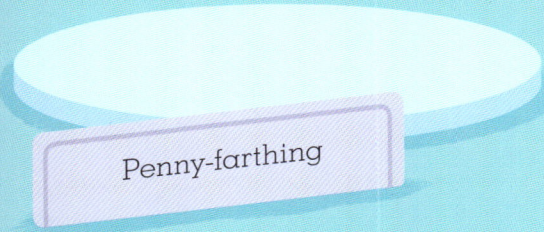

Penny-farthing

Auto-rickshaw

Costume museum

This is where you find out what people wore long ago. Add some more costumes and some children trying on old-fashioned clothes.

THROUGH THE AGES

| 1500s Elizabethan woman | → | 1700s Georgian man | → | 1800s Victorian man | → | 1900s Edwardian woman |

PHOTO CORNER
TRY ON COSTUMES

JAPANESE
GEISHA KIMONO

EUROPEAN
FLAPPER DRESS

INDIAN
WEDDING DRESS

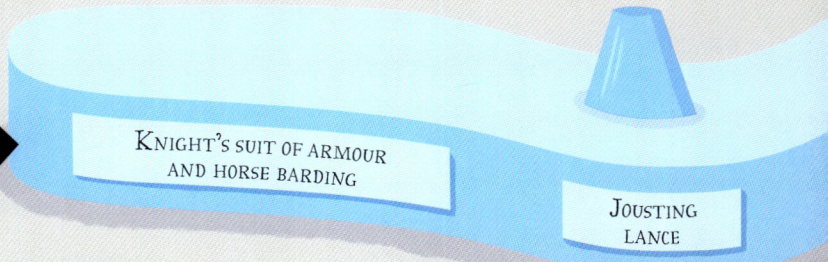

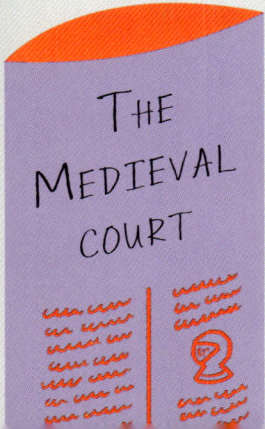

JESTER AND GITTERN

KNIGHT'S SUIT OF ARMOUR
AND HORSE BARDING

JOUSTING
LANCE

THE
MEDIEVAL
COURT

Toy museum

At a toy museum you can see the kinds of toys your grandparents may have played with when they were children. Add more playthings to the windows of the old shop.

Posters

Wooden toys

The Old Toyshop

Classic books

Wind-up toys

Museum objects

Add the stickers for these objects and find matching labels. Can you spot any of these things in the book?

Atom
model

Ammonite
fossil

Toy
vehicles

Egyptian
statue

Canopic
jar

Venetian
mask

String
puppet

Rocket
model

Jester hat

Japanese
fan

Greek
urn

Shekere
rattle

Museums pages 2-3

Canopic jars

Boat model

Box

Pyramid model

Vase

Cat mummies

Mirror

The goddess Isis

Mask

Obelisk

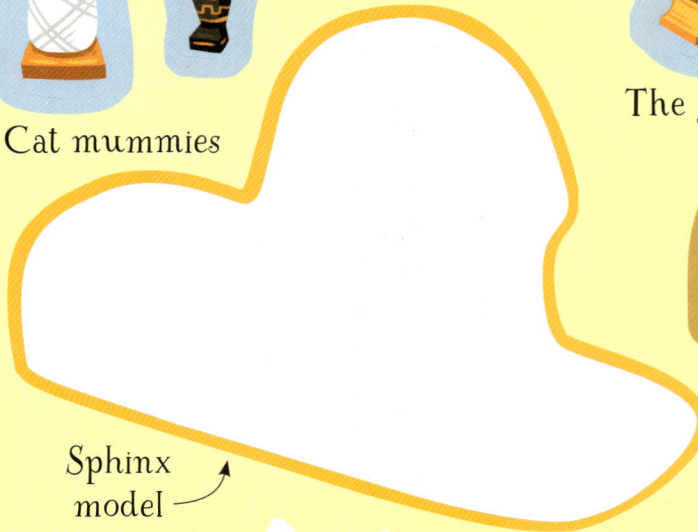

Sphinx model

Sarcophagus

The goddess Bastet

The god Anubis

Science museum

pages 4–5

Humanoid robot

Saturn
and Jupiter

Satellite

Atom model

Van de Graaff
generator

Telescope

DNA
model

Spacesuit

Lunar rover

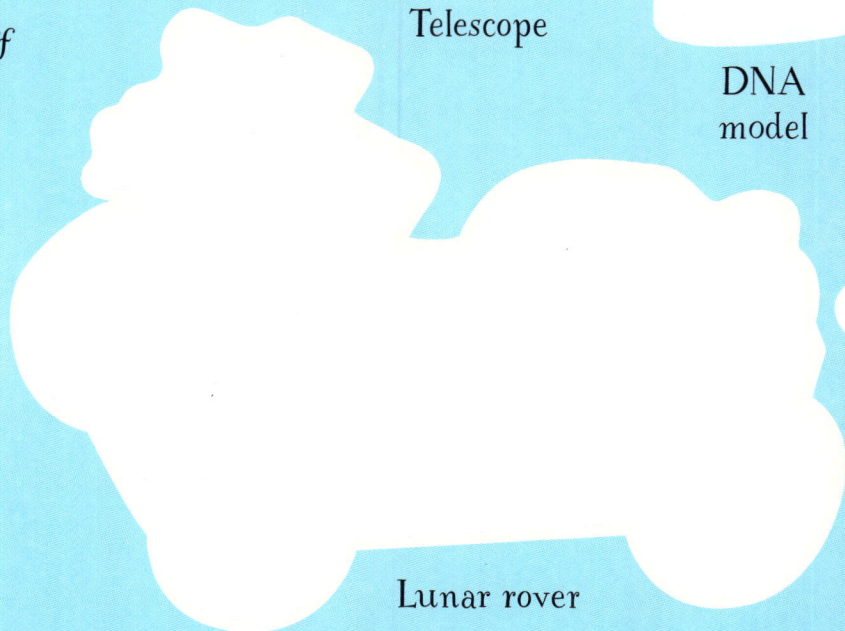

Space rocket

Natural history museum

pages 6-7

Woolly mammoth skeleton model

Ankylosaurus

Pterodactyl

Tyrannosaurus rex

Plesiosaur

Triceratops skull model

Aegyptosaurus tail

Aegyptosaurus head and neck

Around the world

Ancient Greek pottery

Japanese art

Totem pole

Masks

Activity table

African musical instruments

Transport museum

1921 Dennis fire engine

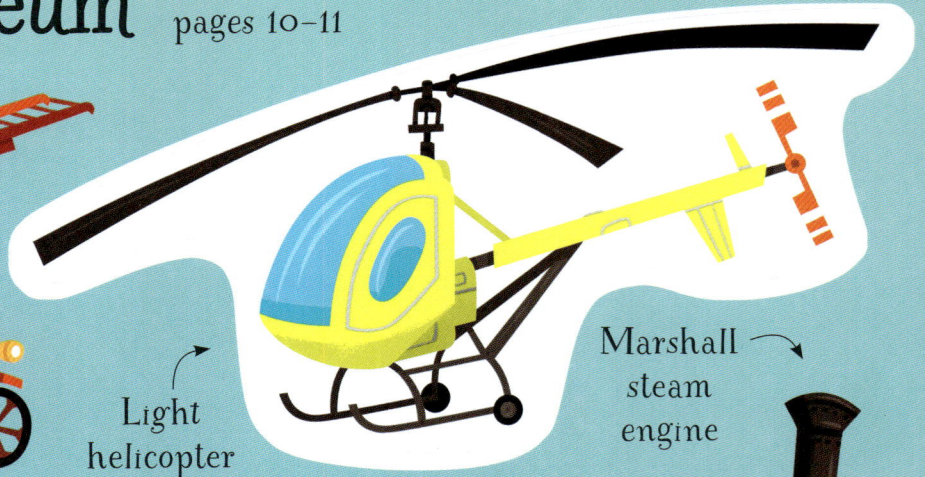

Light helicopter

Marshall steam engine

Auto-rickshaw

Penny-farthing

Ford Model T motorcar

Steam engine

Motorcycle and sidecar

Formula 1 car

Costume museum

pages 12–13

Elizabethan woman

Georgian man

Victorian man

Edwardian woman

Jousting lance

Photographer

Gittern

Suit of armour and barding

Jester

Japanese geisha kimono

Indian wedding dress

Costumes to try on

Toy museum

pages 14–15

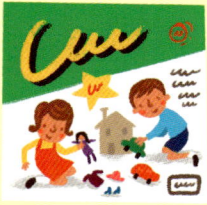   

Posters

Wooden toys

Train

Ship

Teddy bear

Pedalcar

Hobbyhorse

 Doll

Doll's pram

Carousel

Spinning top

Jack-in-the-box

Robot

Doll's house

Wind-up toys

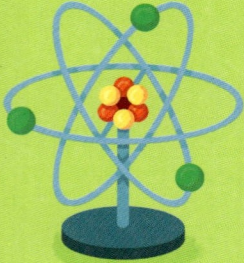

Venetian mask	String puppet	Shekere rattle	Jester hat
Atom model	Japanese fan	Rocket model	Greek urn
Toy vehicles	Egyptian statue	Ammonite fossil	Canopic jar